SOUNDS OF LANGUAGE READERS

Sounds
of the
Storyteller

by Bill Martin, Jr.

Holt, Rinehart and Winston, Inc., New York

Acknowledgments

The following selections are adapted from Little Owl Books copyright © 1963 by Holt,
Rinehart and Winston, Inc., except as noted.

"Getting to Know You," "I Whistle a Happy Tune," pictures, from CHILDREN OF
THE WORLD SAY "GOOD MORNING" by Herbert McClure. Lyrics, "Getting to
Know You," "I Whistle a Happy Tune" by Oscar Hammerstein II, from THE KING
AND I copyright 1951 by Richard Rodgers and Oscar Hammerstein II. Used by permis-
sion of the publishers, Williamson Music, Inc., New York, New York and Chappell &
Co., Ltd.

"Here's a Picture for Storytelling," (page 78) from POEMS FOR COUNTING.

"The Kind of Bath for Me," picture, from THE SUN IS A STAR by Sune Engelbrektson.

"Here's a Picture for Storytelling," (page 248) from TO KNOW A TREE by Thomas
M. O'Brien.

The following selections are adapted from Young Owl Books copyright © 1964 by Holt,
Rinehart and Winston, Inc., except as noted.

"Old Lucy and the Pigeons," from OLD LUCY LINDY by Leland Jacobs.

"Mother Meadowlark and Brother Snake," from MOTHER MEADOWLARK AND
BROTHER SNAKE by Billy Firethunder.

"Here's a Picture for Storytelling," (page 44) from THE FUNNY OLD MAN AND
THE FUNNY OLD WOMAN by Martha Barber.

"Our New Home in the City," from OUR NEW HOME IN THE CITY by Leo Israel.

"Here's a Picture for Storytelling," (page 70) from MY TURTLE TODAY by Edith
G. Stull.

"A Parade," picture; "The Steadfast Tin Soldier," from THE STEADFAST TIN SOL-
DIER by Hans Christian Andersen, translated from the Danish by Carl Malmberg.
Poem, "A Parade" by Mary Catherine Rose, from THE SOUND OF POETRY by Mary
C. Austin and Queenie B. Mills. Copyright © 1963 by Allyn and Bacon, Inc. and reprinted
by permission.

"If You Should Meet a Crocodile," picture, from ELEVEN AND THREE ARE POETRY
compiled by Sally Nohelty.

"Counting Lightly," from COUNTING LIGHTLY by Leonard Simon.

"Paulossie," from PAULOSSIE, AN ESKIMO BOY by Robert C. Swim.

"Here's a Picture for Storytelling," (page 146) from FOUR THREES ARE 12 by H. R.
Wright.

Contents

Sounds
of the
Storyteller

Getting to Know You

Getting to know you, getting to know all about you.
Getting to like you, getting to hope you like me,
Getting to know you, putting it my way, but nicely,
You are precisely my cup of tea!

Getting to know you, getting to feel free and easy
When I am with you, getting to know what to say.
Haven't you noticed? Suddenly I'm bright and breezy,
Because of all the beautiful and new things
I'm learning about you day by day.

by Oscar Hammerstein II

I Whistle a Happy Tune

Whenever I feel afraid,
I hold my head erect
And whistle a happy tune,
So no one will suspect
   I'm afraid.

       by Oscar Hammerstein II

People

Tall people, short people,
Thin people, fat,
Lady so dainty
Wearing a hat,
Straight people,
   dumpy people,
Man dressed in brown,
Baby in a buggy—
These make a town.

       by Lois Lenski

pictures by Herbert McClure

Old Lucy and The Pigeons

by Leland Jacobs,
pictures by Ed Renfro

Old Lucy Lindy lived alone.

She lived alone in an old stone house.

The old house had an old yard.

Around the old yard was an old fence.

Old Lucy Lindy lived alone.

So she talked to herself.

"My!" she said to herself.

"My, my!"

Now, Old Lucy Lindy liked to live alone.

She didn't like dogs.

She didn't like cats.

And *especially* she didn't like pigeons.

"My!" said Old Lucy Lindy to herself.

"I don't like pigeons."

But pigeons came to Lucy Lindy's old house.

They came to her yard.

They came to her fence.

13

Every day Old Lucy Lindy said,

"Go away, pigeons.

Go away from my fence.

Go away from my yard.

Go away from my house."

But every day the pigeons came back.

"My!" said Lucy Lindy to herself.

"What shall I do?"

One morning Old Lucy Lindy said to herself,

"I know what I'll do."

All day she was busy.

She was busy with a hammer.

She was busy with nails.

She was busy with a brush.

Old Lucy Lindy made a sign.

The sign said,

PIGEONS, GO AWAY !

She put the sign in the yard.

Then she went to bed.

The next morning Lucy Lindy went outdoors.

"My, my!" she said to herself.

There were pigeons in the yard.
There were pigeons on the house.
There were pigeons on the fence.
There were even pigeons on the sign.
Old Lucy Lindy looked and looked.
She shook her head.

"My!" said Lucy Lindy to herself.
"What stupid pigeons.

They can't even read!"

PIGEONS,
GO AWAY !

I Have To Have It

I need a little stick when I
Go walking up the street,
To poke in cracks as I go by
Or point at birds up in the sky
Or whack at trees we meet.

I need a stick to zim along
The fences that we pass;
I need a stick for dragging through
The gravel or the grass.

My father says there cannot be
A single doubt about it:
I have to have a stick with me.
I cannot

      walk

         without it.

The Picnic

We brought a rug for sitting on,
Our lunch was in a box.
The sand was warm. We didn't wear
Hats or Shoes or Socks.

Waves came curling up the beach.
We waded. It was fun.
Our sandwiches were different kinds.
I dropped my jelly one.

poems by Dorothy Aldis,
picture by Robert Jon Antler

19

Oh, What a Beautiful Morning!

by Oscar Hammerstein II,
picture by Herbert McClure

There's a bright golden haze
    on the meadow,
There's a bright golden haze
    on the meadow,
The corn is as high
    as an elephant's eye,
An' it looks like it's climbing
    right up in the sky.

Oh, what a beautiful mornin',
Oh, what a beautiful day,
I got a beautiful feelin'
Everything's going my way.

Mother Meadowlark and Brother Snake

by Billy Firethunder,
pictures by John Peterson

Mother Meadowlark awakened one morning
to find a big snake curled around her nest.
Mother Meadowlark was frightened
but she spoke calmly.

"Good morning, Brother Snake,"
said Mother Meadowlark.
"I am glad to see you.
You have not come to visit us for a long time,
so I will make you the best breakfast
that you have ever eaten!"
The snake flicked his tongue
and looked hungrily at Mother Meadowlark.

"But, unfortunately, Brother Snake,"
said Mother Meadowlark,
"a neighbor borrowed my big brass kettle,
just yesterday.
I will send one of my children to fetch it.

When he returns," said Mother Meadowlark,
"I will cook you the best breakfast
that you have ever eaten."

Mother Meadowlark nudged the baby birds
that were sleeping under her wings.
"Wake up, children," she said.
"Brother Snake has come to visit us."

Four little meadowlarks pushed their sleepy heads
out from under their mother's wing.
When they saw the big snake,
they were frightened but they stayed calm,
just like their mother.

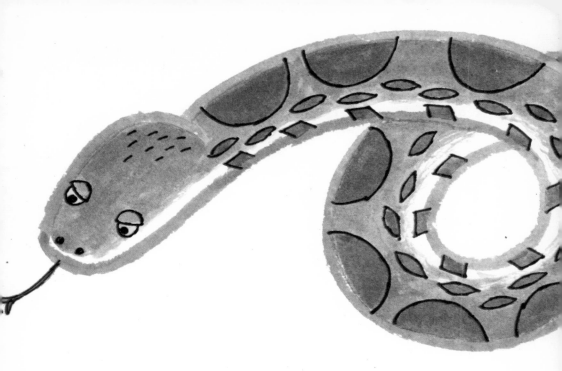

"All of my children are named after you,
Brother Snake,"
said Mother Meadowlark.
"This is my first child.
He is named Scaly-Skin.
I will send him to the neighbors
to bring back my brass kettle."

Mother Meadowlark gave the first baby bird
a little nudge.
He hopped to the edge of the nest.

"Good morning, Brother Snake,"
he said politely.

The snake flicked his tongue
and looked hungrily
at the first baby bird.

"Be off now, Scaly-Skin,"
said Mother Meadowlark,
"and bring back my brass kettle."

Mother Meadowlark gave the first baby bird
another little nudge,
and he lifted his wings
and flew quickly out of the nest.
He landed about thirty feet away
in the tall grass.

Then Mother Meadowlark said,
"My second child is also named after you,
Brother Snake.
I call him Beady-Eyes."
    Mother Meadowlark gave the second baby bird
a little nudge.
    He hopped to the edge of the nest.

"Good morning, Brother Snake,"
he said politely.

The snake flicked his tongue hungrily
at the second baby bird.

"I wonder what is keeping Scaly-Skin so long,"
said Mother Meadowlark.
"Beady Eyes,
you'd better go over there
and help him.
Maybe the brass kettle is too heavy
for him to carry."

Mother Meadowlark gave the second baby bird
another little nudge,
and he lifted his wings
and quickly flew out of the nest.
He landed about thirty feet away
in the tall grass.

No sooner had he landed
than Mother Meadowlark said,
"This is my third child,
Brother Snake.
I also named her after you.
She is called Creep-Along."

Mother Meadowlark gave the third baby bird
a little nudge.
She hopped to the edge of the nest.

"Good morning, Brother Snake,"
she said politely.

The snake flicked his tongue
and looked hungrily
at the third baby bird.

Mother Meadowlark said,
"Creep-Along,
   go tell the boys to hurry.
   I know that my Brother
   is hungry and is waiting
   for his breakfast."

Mother Meadowlark
gave the third baby bird
another little nudge.
The third baby bird lifted her wings
and quickly flew out of the nest.
She landed in the tall grass
thirty feet away.

No sooner had she landed
than Mother Meadowlark said,
"I wonder what can be keeping
the children so long.
They must be playing along the way.
I should have sent No-Ears.
She also is named after you,
Brother Snake.
She is the only one of my children
who usually does what she's told."

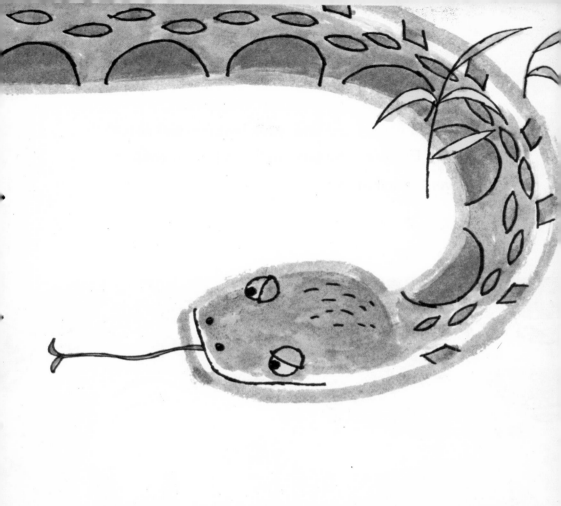

Mother Meadowlark gave the fourth baby bird
a little nudge.
She hopped to the edge of the nest.
"Good morning, Brother Snake,"
she said politely.
The snake flicked his tongue
and looked hungrily
at the fourth baby bird.

"No-Ears," said Mother Meadowlark,
"would you go and find your brothers and sister?
My Brother is hungry and wants his breakfast
very much indeed."

Mother Meadowlark gave the fourth baby bird
another little nudge.
She lifted her wings and flew out of the nest,
into the tall grass.

As soon as she had left the nest,
Mother Meadowlark said,
"Farewell, Brother Snake.
You are not going to get any breakfast."

Then she, too, flew away to join her children in the safety of the tall grass.

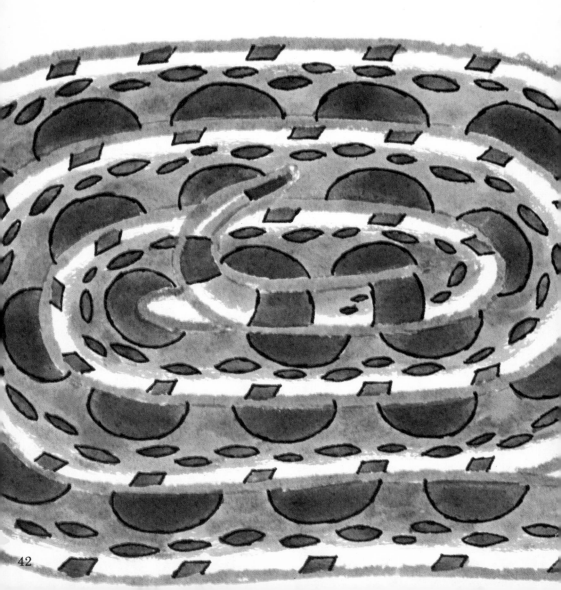

And...

brother snake
went home hungry
that night.

Here's a Picture for Storytelling

by Ed Renfro

Moving

I like to move. There's such a feeling
of hurrying
  and scurrying.
And such a feeling
Of men with trunks and packing cases,
Of kitchen clocks and mother's laces,
Dusters, dishes, books and vases,
Toys and pans and candles.

I always find things I'd forgotten,
An old brown Teddy stuffed with cotton,
Some croquet mallets without handles,
A marble and my worn-out sandals,
A half an engine and a hat . . .
And I like that.

I like to watch the big vans backing,
And the lumbering
  and the cumbering,
And the hammering and the tacking.
I even like the packing!

And that will prove
I like to move.

by Eunice Tietjens

Our New Home in the City

by Leo Israel,
pictures by Ruth Ruhman

My name is Peter.
My family and I are driving
to our new home in the city.

We ride over a bridge and through a park.

"Here we are," says mother.

"This is our new home in the city."

We stop in front of a tall building.

It is an apartment house.

Many families live in the apartment house.

We enter the front door of the apartment house.
Judy and I and Brownie find the elevator
that will take us up to our new home.

Mother and father find the button
that rings the doorbell in our apartment.
They also find the mailbox
in the lobby of the apartment house.

We ride the elevator up to our new home.
It is on the fourth floor of the apartment house.
"Our new home is way up high," says Judy.
From the window I can see many children
on the playground below.

In the hall outside our apartment,
Judy and I find where we will put our garbage.
The garbage falls down a chute to the basement
where it is burned.

In the basement of the apartment house,
Judy and I find the laundry room
where mother will do our washing.

We find the workroom
where the building superintendent fixes things.
We also see a storeroom
for bicycles and baby carriages.

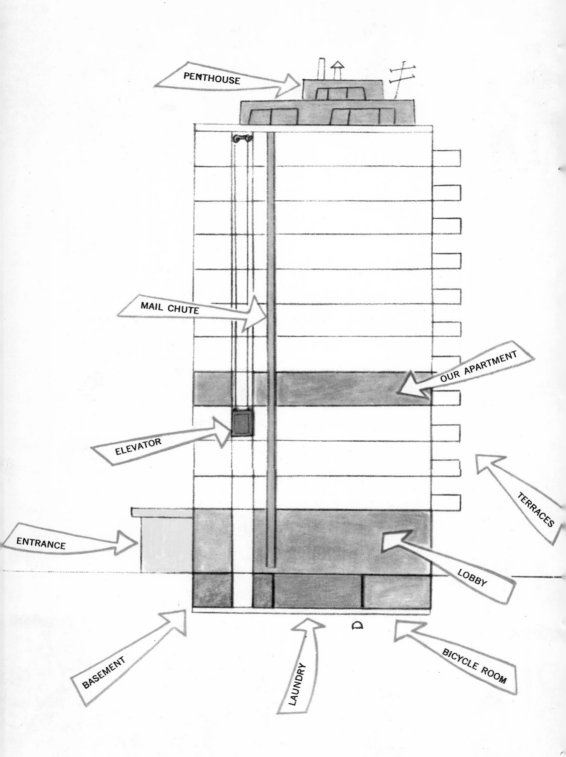

PENTHOUSE

MAIL CHUTE

OUR APARTMENT

ELEVATOR

TERRACES

ENTRANCE

LOBBY

BASEMENT

LAUNDRY

BICYCLE ROOM

56

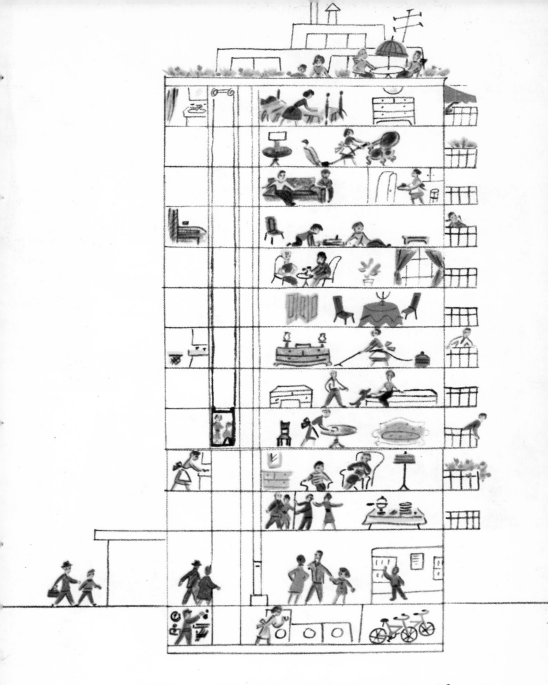

Here are two pictures of the apartment house.

Can you find where Judy and I live?

Can you count how many families live

in the apartment house?

Judy and I get on a bus that stops near our new home.

The bus takes us past a city park.
We pass a public library and some stores.

"This is our new school," Judy says.
"We will get off the bus here."

We meet our new teachers at the school.
Some of the school children live in our apartment house.

On the way home from school we stop at the library.
We sign our names for library cards
so that we can borrow books to read.

We walk past all kinds of stores.
Many people are shopping in the stores.

A policeman helps us cross the street safely.

We see many children on the city street.

Judy and I hope they will be our friends.

The cars on the city street are noisy.

The drivers honk their horns because they are in a hurry.

When we arrive back at the apartment house,
we ride the elevator up to the fourth floor.
Mother is preparing our dinner and father is with her.
Judy and I help.

At night we watch the lights go on
all over the city . . .
in the park, on the river,
on the bridge, and in the tall buildings.
We like our new home in the apartment house.
When you come to the city,
we hope you will visit us.

Look, Edwin!

Do you see that boy
Talking to the other boy?
No, over there by those two men—
Wait, don't look now—now look again.
No, not the one in navy-blue;
That's the one he's talking to.
Sure you see him? Striped pants?
Well, *he was born in Paris, France.*

by Edna St. Vincent Millay,
picture by Robert Jon Antler

Here's a Picture for Storytelling

by Mamoru Funai

Boxer Lies Here
He was a good
turtle

The King's Breakfast

by A. A. Milne,
pictures by Ernest Shepard

The King asked
The Queen, and
The Queen asked
The Dairymaid:
"Could we have some butter for
The Royal slice of bread?"
The Queen asked
The Dairymaid,
The Dairymaid
Said, "Certainly,
I'll go and tell
The cow
Now
Before she goes to bed."

The Dairymaid
She curtsied,

And went and told
The Alderney:
"Don't forget the butter for
The Royal slice of bread."

The Alderney
Said sleepily:
"You'd better tell
His Majesty
That many people nowadays
Like marmalade
Instead."

The Dairymaid
Said, "Fancy!"
And went to
Her Majesty.
She curtsied to the Queen, and
She turned a little red:
"Excuse me,
Your Majesty,
For taking of
The liberty,
But marmalade is tasty, if
It's very
Thickly
Spread."

The Queen said
"Oh!"
And went to
His Majesty:
"Talking of the butter for
The Royal slice of bread,
Many people
Think that
Marmalade
Is nicer.
Would you like to try a little
Marmalade
Instead?"

The King said,
"Bother!"
And then he said,
"Oh, deary me!"
The King sobbed, "Oh, deary me!"
And went back to bed.
"Nobody,"
He whimpered
"Could call me
A fussy man;
I *only* want
A little bit
Of butter for
My bread!"

The Queen said,
"There, there!"
And went to
The Dairymaid.

The Dairymaid
Said, "There, there!"
And went to the shed.

The cow said,
"There, there!
I didn't really
Mean it;
Here's milk for his porringer
And butter for his bread."

The Queen took
The butter
And brought it to
His Majesty;

The King said,
"Butter, eh?"
And bounced out of bed.
"Nobody," he said,
As he kissed her
Tenderly,
"Nobody," he said,
As he slid down
The banisters,
"Nobody,
My darling,
Could call me
A fussy man—

BUT

I do like a little bit of butter to my bread!"

Here's a Picture for Storytelling

by Robert M. Quackenbush

A Parade

A parade!   A parade!

A-rum-a-tee-tum

I know a parade

By the sound of the drum.

    A-rum-a-tee-tum

    A-rum-a-tee-tum

    A-rum-a-tee-tum-

    a-tee-tum.

Here it comes.

Down the street.

I know a parade

By the sound of the feet.

Music and feet

Music and feet

Can't you feel

The sound and the beat?

    A-rum-a-tee-tum

    A-rum-a-tee-tum

    A-rum-a-tee-tum-

    a-tee-tum.

by Mary Catherine Rose,
picture by Robert M. Quackenbush

The Steadfast Tin Soldier

by Hans Christian Andersen,
translated by Carl Malmburg,
pictures by Robert M. Quackenbush

Once upon a time there were twenty-five tin soldiers. They were all brothers, for they had been made from the same old tin spoon.

Each one stood stiffly at attention, looking straight ahead and keeping his rifle shouldered. And they all looked very smart in their red and blue uniforms.

The very first thing they heard in this world, when the lid was taken off their box, was a little boy clapping his hands and exclaiming, "Tin soldiers!"

They had been given to him as a birthday present, and he immediately set them up on the table. Each soldier looked exactly like the others, except for one,

who was just a little different. He had only one leg, for he had been poured into the mold last of all and there had not been quite enough tin to finish him. Nevertheless, he stood just as firmly on one leg as the others did on their two, and of all the soldiers he was the one that people would some day hear about.

On the table there were many other toys, but what caught the eye first was a fine paper castle with tiny windows, through which you could look and see the rooms inside. Outside the castle, little trees had been placed around a mirror which was a make-believe lake. Wax swans floated on the surface of the mirror and were reflected in it. It was all very charming, but prettiest of all was a little lady who stood in the open doorway of the castle.

She too was cut out of paper, but wore a skirt of sheerest linen, and over her shoulder was draped a narrow blue ribbon on which glittered a spangle as big as her face. The little lady held both her arms outstretched, for she was a dancer, and she had kicked one leg so high into the air that the tin soldier could not see it. So he thought that she, too, had only one leg, as he did.

"Now, that's the very wife for me!" he thought.
"But she is a lady of high rank and lives in a castle,
whereas I have only a box, and there are twenty-five
of us sharing that. No, that would be no place for her!
But anyway, I must try to make her acquaintance."

Then he stretched out behind a snuffbox that stood
on the table. From there he could watch the charming little lady who stood on one leg without ever
losing her balance.

Late in the evening the other tin soldiers were put
back into the box, and the people in the house went
to bed. Then the toys began to play. They played
paying visits, fighting battles, and giving parties.

The tin soldiers rattled around in their box, for they wanted to join in the fun, but they could not lift the lid. The nutcracker turned somersaults and the slate pencil scribbled on the slate. There was such a commotion that the canary woke up and began to join in the conversation—in verse, if you can believe such a thing! The only two who did not stir were the tin soldier and the little dancer. She remained poised on the tip of her toe with both her arms outstretched. He stood steadfastly on his one leg and did not for a moment take his eyes off her.

Then the clock struck midnight and—pop!—up snapped the lid of the snuff-box! But there was no snuff in it—instead, there was a little goblin. It was a trick snuffbox, you see, meant to startle people.

"Tin soldier," said the goblin, "you had better keep your eyes to yourself!" But the tin soldier pretended not to hear.

"All right!" said the goblin. "You just wait until tomorrow!"

The next morning, after the children got up, the tin soldier was moved over to the window sill. Whether what happened next was the work of the goblin or of a gust of wind, we do not know, but suddenly the window flew open, and the soldier fell headlong from the third story. It was a terrifying fall. He landed with his head down, his one leg up in the air, and his bayonet stuck between two paving stones.

The housemaid and the little boy ran down at once to look for him, but although they almost stepped on him, they did not see him. If the tin soldier had cried out, "Here I am!" they would surely have found him, but he did not think it was proper to shout when he was in uniform.

Soon it began to rain. The raindrops fell faster and faster, until it was a regular downpour. When the storm was over, two street urchins came along.

"Look!" one of them said. "There's a tin soldier! Let's send him for a sail."

So they made a boat out of an old newspaper, and put the tin soldier inside. Away he sailed down the gutter, while the boys ran along beside him clapping their hands. Goodness, what great waves there were in the gutter, and what a swift current! The paper boat pitched and tossed and whirled so fast that the tin soldier became quite dizzy. But he did not flinch or show the least sign of fear. He looked straight ahead and kept a firm hold on his rifle.

All of a sudden the boat was swept into a long drain pipe. There it was as dark as it had been in his box.

"I wonder where I'm headed," the tin soldier thought. "If only I had the little lady here in the boat with me, it might be twice as dark and I shouldn't mind it a bit!"

Just at that moment there appeared a huge water rat who lived in the pipe.

"Have you a passport?" asked the rat. "Hand it over!"

The tin soldier did not answer, but clasped his rifle tighter than ever. The boat rushed on with the rat close behind it. Oh, how he gnashed his teeth and shouted to the sticks and straws floating in the stream: "Stop him! Stop him! He didn't pay his toll! He wouldn't show his passport!"

The current grew swifter and swifter. Now the tin soldier could see daylight ahead, but he heard a roaring noise that was enough to frighten even the bravest of men. Just think! Where the pipe ended, the water emptied into a big canal. The tin soldier felt as frightened as you and I would if we were about to be swept over a huge waterfall.

But now he was so close to the edge that he could not escape. The boat shot out into the canal, while the tin soldier held himself as straight as he could— nobody could say of him that he had so much as blinked an eye.

The boat spun around three or four times and filled with water to the brim. It was sure to sink. The tin soldier soon stood in water up to his neck, and the boat sank deeper and deeper. Now the paper began to come apart. The soldier felt the water swirling about his head, and as he went under he thought of the lovely little dancer whom he would never see again. In his ears rang the words of an old song:

"Onward! Danger calls you, soldier!
Death awaits you in the field!"

Now the paper boat gave way entirely, and the tin soldier plunged through the bottom. Just then a big fish came along and swallowed him.

My, how dark it was in the fish! It was even darker than it had been in the pipe! And how dreadfully cramped! But the tin soldier remained as steadfast as ever, lying at full length with his rifle still shouldered.

The fish thrashed about in a most frightful manner. Then, finally, it became very quiet.

After some time, a flash of lightning seemed to penetrate the darkness. Suddenly it was daylight again, and someone exclaimed, "A tin soldier!" The fish had been caught, taken to market and sold, and

was now in the kitchen where the maid had just cut it open with a big knife. She picked the soldier up by the waist, and with two fingers carried him into the living room.

Everyone was eager to get a look at such a remarkable fellow—a tin soldier who had traveled around in the belly of a fish!

But the tin soldier did not let their admiration go to his head. They set him up on the table, and then —what strange things do happen in this world!— he found he was in the very same room that he had been in before. He saw the very same children. The very same toys stood on the table — there was the splendid castle, and the lovely little dancer. She was still standing poised on one leg with the other high in the air. Yes, she was steadfast, too. The tin soldier was so deeply moved that he almost shed tin tears, but that of course was something a soldier could never do. So he gazed at her and she gazed at him, but neither of them said a word.

At that moment, for no reason at all, the little boy picked up the tin soldier and threw him into the fireplace. Without doubt, it was the goblin in the snuffbox who was to blame for it.

The tin soldier stood there lit up by the flames. He began to feel terribly hot, but whether the heat came from the fire, or from the love burning within him, he did not know. The bright colors were gone from his uniform; whether because of all he had been through or because of grief, who can tell? He gazed at the little lady and she gazed at him. He felt himself melting away, but he remained steadfast, standing at attention, shouldering his rifle.

Suddenly a door was opened. A gust of air caught the little dancer, and, like a sylph, she fluttered into the fire and landed right next to the tin soldier. She burst into flame and was gone!

The tin soldier melted down to a lump, and the next day, when the house-maid emptied the ashes, she found him in the shape of a little tin heart. But all that was left of the dancer was her spangle, and that was burnt black as coal.

Little Orphant Annie

by James Whitcomb Riley,
pictures by Ken Longtemps

Little Orphant Annie's
   come to our house to stay,
An' wash the cups and saucers up,
   an' brush the crumbs away,
An' shoo the chickens off the porch,
   an' dust the hearth, an' sweep,
An' make the fire, an' bake the bread,
   an' earn her board-an'-keep;
An' all us other children, when the
   supper things is done,
We set around the kitchen fire
   an' has the mostest fun
A-list'nin' to the witch tales 'at Annie tells about,
An' the Gobble-uns 'at gits you
        Ef you   Don't   Watch   Out!

Onc't they was a little boy
    wouldn't say his prayers,—
So when he went to bed at night,
    away upstairs,
His Mammy heerd him hollar,
    an' his Daddy heerd him bawl,
An' when they turn't the kivvers down,
    he wasn't there at all!

An' they seeked him in the rafter room,
    an' cubbyhole, an press,
An' seeked him up the chimbly flue,
    an' ever'wheres, I guess;
But all they ever found was thist his pants
    an' roundabout:—
An' the Gobble-uns 'll git you
          Ef you
         Don't
          Watch
          Out!

An' one time a little girl 'ud allus laugh an' grin,
An' make fun of ever'one,
   an' all her blood an' kin;
An' onc't, when they was "company,"
   an' ole folks was there,
She mocked 'em an' shocked 'em,
   an' said she didn't care!
An' thist as she kicked her heels,
   an' turn't to run an' hide,
They was two great big Black Things
   a-standin' by her side,
An' they snatched her through the ceilin'
   'fore she knowed what she's about!
An' the Gobble-uns 'll git you
      Ef you
        Don't
          Watch
            Out!

An' little Orphant Annie says,

An' little Orphant Annie says,
 when the blaze is blue,
An' the lamp-wick sputters,
 an' the wind goes woo-oo!
An' you hear the crickets quit,
 an' the moon is gray,
An' the lightin' bugs in dew
 is all squenched away,—
You better mind yer parents, and yer teachers
 fond an' dear,
An' churish them 'at loves you,
 an' dry the orphant's tear,
An' he'p the pore an' needy ones
 'at clusters all about,
Er the Gobble-uns 'll get you
      Ef you
       Don't
        Watch
         Out!

If you should meet a crocodile

Don't take a stick and poke him;
Ignore the welcome in his smile,
Be careful not to stroke him.
For as he sleeps upon the Nile,
He thinner gets and thinner;
And whene'er you meet a Crocodile
He's ready for his dinner.

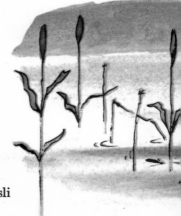

author unknown,
picture by Kelly Oechsli

The Dinosaur

A beast of yore,
Doesn't live here
Any more.

by Carl S. Junge,
picture by Robert Jon Antler

Counting Lightly

by Leonard Simon,
pictures by Ted Schroeder

Father: "Come on, Dim. It's time to go.

Today you will learn to be a hunter."

Dim: "Today is the day," thought Dim.

"I will be a great hunter like my father.

I'm coming, Father! I'm ready!"

Father: "And what are you going to do with that spear, Dim?"

Dim: "I'm going to hunt buffalo."

Father: "Yes, but first you must learn to find them.

Do you see that tree?

Go hide under it.

If you see any buffalo, come back and tell me."

Reading aloud:
You understand,
don't you,
that if you read
this story as a play,
you will leave out
phrases like
Dim thought,
he said, etc.

Dim: "Whew! It's hot up here!" thought Dim.
"Hunting is hard work.
I haven't seen a buffalo all day.
Gee, I'm tired.
Maybe I can take a little nap."

Dim jumped up.

Dim: "What was that?

What makes the earth shake so?

I see them now.

There are the buffalo.

There are so many of them.

There are more than a dog has legs!

There are more than I have friends!

I must tell everybody!"

                    Dim ran down the hill.

Dim: "I found them!

             I found the buffalo!" he shouted.

Father: "How many, Dim? How many did you see?"

Dim: "I saw more than a tree has branches,

             more than there are stars in the sky."

Sister: "Oh Dim, you did not," said his sister.

             "You're just making it up."

Dim: "I am not!" said Dim.

             "I saw a whole bunch."

Sister: "How many?"

Dim: "I don't know."

Father: "Dim," said his father, "a great hunter must know

             how many animals he sees."

Dim: "All right. I'll go back and look,

             and then I'll tell you how many."

Dim: "But how can I count all the buffalo?" thought Dim.

"I wish I could carry each buffalo back.

That way I would not have to count them.

But they are too heavy.

A stage direction: I will never be able to be a hunter."

Dim sat down on the hillside.

Dim: "Lying on the rocks hurts my knees.

The rocks! That gives me an idea!

I know how I can count the buffalo."

Announcer: How do you think Dim will count the buffalo?

114

Dim: "I cannot carry buffalo.
But I can carry rocks.
One rock for one buffalo.
Another rock for another buffalo.
This is easy.
Now, all I have to do is carry the rocks
down the hill."

Dim: "These rocks are heavy," said Dim.

"I don't think I can carry them all."

It's hard to carry rocks

and slide down the hill at the same time.

Oops, dropped one.

Oops, there goes another!

I can't carry so many in my hands.

I saw more buffalo than I have rocks.

I dropped buffalos...I mean

A stage direction: I dropped rocks all the way down the hill."

Everybody laughed.

Father: "Dim, isn't there something lighter than rocks

that you could carry?"

Dim: Dim thought, "I always carry wood for the fire."

"I know," he said.

"I'll carry back a stick of wood for each buffalo.

There are many sticks up on the hill."

Dim: "This is easy," said Dim.

"One stick for one buffalo.

Two sticks for two buffalo.

Another stick for another buffalo."

A stage direction: Soon Dim had a pile of sticks—

one stick for each buffalo.

Dim: "This pile of sticks is hard to carry.

There, I came all the way down the hill

and didn't drop one.

Now, everybody can count my sticks.

The number of sticks is the same

as the number of buffalo."

Dim: "I saw as many buffalo as I have sticks," said Dim.

"Now you can see how many buffalo there are.

But my arms hurt from carrying the sticks.

I'm getting too tired to hunt.

I wish there were a lighter way to count."

Sister: "Dim," said his sister,

"you could count the buffalo with only one stick."

Dim: "I could not!" said Dim. "There are many buffalo."

Sister: "Come on," said his sister, "I'll show you.

Just bring that long stick and that rock."

Announcer: Can you guess how Dim's sister

will count the buffalo?

Sister: "Now Dim, you watch," said his sister.

"There is one buffalo.

I make one mark on the stick.

There is another buffalo.

I make another mark on the stick."

Dim: 'Now I see," said Dim. "I can do the rest."

**A stage
direction:** Dim brought his stick to his father.

Dim: "See how many buffalo there are!

And it isn't so hard to carry just one stick."

Sister: "Dim," said his sister, "you can count
without carrying anything."

Dim: "Count without carrying anything? How?"

Sister: "Use your fingers. Look, Dim!

One finger for one buffalo.

Two fingers for two buffalo.

Another finger for another buffalo."

Dim: "Is that so! But I don't *have* enough fingers

to tell how many buffalo I saw."

Sister: "It doesn't matter, Dim.

When you use up all your fingers,

you can start over again."

Dim: "That's silly."

Sister: "When you use up all your fingers,

just think *all*.

Here, I'll draw a picture to show you.

See, these are like the marks on the stick.

This many means *all*.

So, you saw *all*-and-two buffalo."

A stage direction:

Dim looked at his sister.

He looked at the picture of the stick.

ALL

Dim: "You never use rocks, or sticks, or fingers.

How come you can count?"

Sister: "Oh, I use words," said his sister.

"I made up names to count with.

And using counting names is easy —
all you have to do is remember them.
You can think them, and say them,
and write them, and read them.
And they are never heavy to carry."

Dim: "And then," said Dim,

"you really are counting lightly."

Circus

The band blares
    The naphtha flares,
        The sawdust smells,
    Showmen ring bells,
And oh! right into the circus ring
Comes such a lovely, lovely thing,
     A milk-white pony with flying tress,
    And a beautiful lady,
      A beautiful lady,
        A *beautiful* lady in a pink dress!
The red-and-white clown
For joy tumbles down.
    Like a pink rose
       Round she goes
         On her tiptoes
       With the pony under —
    And then, oh, wonder!
The pony his milk-white tresses droops,
And the beautiful lady,
    The *beautiful* lady,
       Flies like a bird through the paper hoops!
The red-and-white clown for joy falls dead,
Then he waggles his feet and stands on his head,
And the little boys on the two penny seats
Scream with laughter and suck their sweets.

          by Eleanor Farjeon,   picture by Robert Lee

The Snare

I hear a sudden cry of pain!
　　There is a rabbit in a snare:
Now I hear the cry again,
　　But I cannot tell from where.

But I cannot tell from where
　　He is calling out for aid;
Crying on the frightened air,
　　Making everything afraid,

Making everything afraid
　　Wrinkling up his little face,
As he cries again for aid;
　　—And I cannot find the place!

And I cannot find the place
　　Where his paw is in the snare;
Little one! Oh, little one!
　　I am searching everywhere!

by James Stephens,
picture by Cynthia Koehler

Paulossie, an Eskimo Boy

story and photographs of Eskimo stone carvings
by Robert C. Swim

This is Paulossie. He lives in the North, where the wind blows strong and cold. But Paulossie is not cold. He wears the sealskin parka and the sealskin boots called "komiks" that his mother made for him.

Paulossie's father, Tagoona, is a good hunter. He has a pair of good binoculars and a powerful rifle. One day Paulossie borrowed his father's binoculars and went up to the high rocky hill behind his igloo. He wanted to watch the animals that lived on the ice.

Through the binoculars Paulossie watched two walruses sleeping on the ice. Suddenly he saw a great polar bear swimming toward the two sleeping walruses. The polar bear swam closer to the ice. He climbed onto the ice and with his mouth grabbed the nearest walrus by the nose and mouth, so that the walrus could not use its sharp tusks.

The walrus cried out, and fought the polar bear.
But he was caught. The other walrus woke up, and
slipped quickly into the water. There was nothing
he could do to help his friend. It was too late. The
polar bear was going to have his dinner.

"The poor walrus," thought Paulossie.

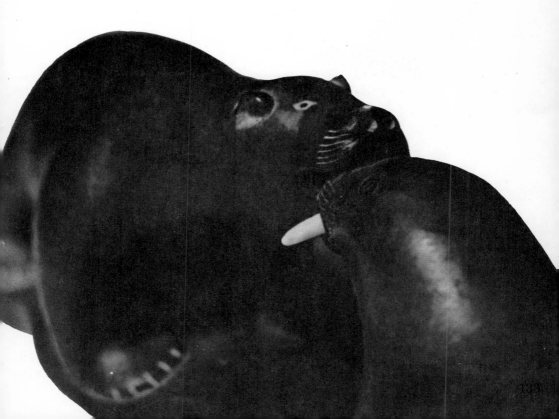

Paulossie picked up the binoculars and looked down on the lake at the foot of the hill. He saw a little duck, swimming alone. Suddenly a snowy white owl swooped down from the sky. The duck dived under the water, but too late. The owl caught the duck by the back of the neck and lifted him out of the water.

"The poor duck," thought Paulossie.

Paulossie stood up and started down the hill. He felt very sorry about the walrus and about the duck.

At the bottom of the hill, Paulossie saw Niki, one of his father's dogs. Niki was chewing on a piece of ice-covered fish. Tagoona, Paulossie's father, had caught the fish through a hole in the ice, and it had frozen solid as soon as it was taken from the water.

The fish Niki ate were always frozen. He had to work hard for every bite.

Paulossie said, "Hello, Niki." But as Paulossie came closer, Niki growled. Niki did not like to have anyone near him when he was eating. He was afraid his food would be taken away from him.

"It is a very hard world," said Paulossie. "First I saw the polar bear attack the walrus. Then I saw the snowy white owl attack the little duck. And now here is Niki, growling because he is afraid I will take his fish."

When Paulossie arrived home, his mother, Mary, was sitting in front of the igloo. She was working very hard. She was chewing a piece of sealskin to make it soft.

This did not seem strange to Paulossie. He had often seen his mother chewing sealskin. She was getting this piece of sealskin ready to make into komiks for Paulossie's little brother, Davidie.

If Mary didn't chew the sealskin, it would be too tough to make into komiks. It would cut the threads when she sewed it, and the water would seep through and wet little Davidie's feet. So Mary had to make the sealskin soft before she sewed it.

Mary looked up as Paulossie came near the igloo. "You look sad, Paulossie," she said. "What is the matter?"

"I think it is a very hard world, Mother," said Paulossie.

"This morning I saw a polar bear attack a walrus that was sleeping on the ice. I saw a snowy white owl swoop down on a little duck. Then Niki growled at me when I came near him while he was eating a fish. Why is it that way?"

Mary slowly pushed back the hood of her parka. Quietly she began, "Do you remember when you were a baby, how you cried when we had no food to give you?"

"No," said Paulossie. "I was too little to remember."

Mary said, "Do you remember when you were a small boy, and your father could not catch any animals or fish? Do you remember how you cried from the pains in your stomach?"

"Yes," said Paulossie, "I remember that."

"Within all creatures," said Mary, "there is a voice that cries, 'Live! Live! Live!' When we do not listen to that voice, it makes us hear it in another way. All creatures have pain when they are hungry, or when they are very tired, or when they are cold.

"If we do not have enough to eat, our stomachs pinch and hurt us. If we do not get enough sleep, our eyes and our head hurt. If we do not dress warmly enough, we shiver and shake, and our teeth begin to chatter.

"Many times," Paulossie's mother continued, "you have seen your father stand beside a hole in the ice for hours and hours. Do you know why he stands there, out in the cold?"

"Yes, I know," said Paulossie. "He is trying to catch a seal."

"Yes," said Mary. "He is waiting for a seal to come up for air. When things go well, your father is able to harpoon a seal.

"Then he brings the seal out of the water, quickly, before it can sink, and he cleans it right there on the ice. If he waited it would freeze solid, and he would not be able to cut the seal with his knife.

"Then he sews it up, puts it on the sled, and brings it home.

"That is how we get sealskins to make into clothing, and oil for our fire, and food for our hungry stomachs.

"If your father did not harpoon the seal, Paulossie, we would not be able to live.

"That is also why he traps the fox, and goes out in his kayak to harpoon the whale and the walrus."

"All creatures want to live," Mary continued. "The polar bear attacks the walrus because he wants to live. The owl attacks the little duck and hungry Niki guards his food because they want to live. And your father stands out in the cold, near a hole in the ice, waiting to harpoon a seal, because he wants to live.

"When we are young, our parents help us to stay alive. When we grow older, we must take care of ourselves. One day soon, Paulossie, you will go with your father to harpoon the whale and the walrus, for you, too, must learn how to keep yourself alive."

Just then little Davidie came out of the igloo.
He came out to see if his komiks were finished. But
he was not dressed for the cold air.

"Paulossie," said Mary, "will you take Davidie back inside the igloo, please? I will finish his boots for him. He is in a hurry for them."

"Yes, I will, Mother," said Paulossie.

Paulossie took Davidie inside the igloo. Mary finished softening the sealskin for little Davidie's komiks. Paulossie played with his little brother while they waited for Tagoona to come home with something to eat. Already Paulossie's stomach was telling him it was time for supper.

Here's a Picture for Storytelling

by Margaret Soucheck Cranstoun

The Kind of Bath for Me

You can take a tub with a rub and a scrub
    in a two-foot tank of tin,
You can stand and look at the whirling brook
    and think about jumping in;
You can chatter and shake in the cold black lake,
    but the kind of bath for me,
Is to take a dip from the side of a ship,
    in the trough of the rolling sea.

You may lie and dream in the bed of a stream
    when an August day is dawning,
Or believe 'tis nice to break the ice
    on your tub of a winter morning;
You may sit and shiver beside the river,
    but the kind of bath for me,
Is to take a dip from the side of a ship,
    in the trough of the rolling sea.

by Sir Edward Parry,
picture by Eric Carle

Here's a Picture for Storytelling

by Leo Summers

The Story of Tom Thumb

traditional, adapted by Bill Martin, Jr.,
pictures by John Peterson

Once on a cold winter night long, long ago, a woodcutter sat by the fire, stirring the flames with a stick. His wife sat near him, at her spinning wheel, working.

"Oh, I wish we had a child," he said. "All I hear is the sound of the wind whistling at the door. I would much rather hear the sound of children playing on the floor."

"Yah, yah," said his wife. "If only we had a child, even if he were no bigger than my thumb, that would be having my heart's desire."

In due time, a child was born to the woodcutter and his wife, and though he was perfect in every way, alas! he was no bigger than his mother's thumb. He was so small that his mother could cradle him in the palm of her hand.

"Oh, what a beautiful child he is," said the wood-cutter's wife.

"Yah, yah," said the woodcutter. "He's the hand-somest child in the village."

Though they fed him plenty of rich nourishment, he grew no larger and remained always the size that he was first born, no larger than his mother's thumb. And they called him *Tom Thumb*.

One day many years later, when Tom's father was going into the forest to cut wood, he chanced to say, "Oh, if only I had someone who could bring the horse and the cart to me this afternoon, it would make my work so much easier."

"I can bring the horse and cart to you, Father," said Tom.

"How could you do that, Tom? You are so little, you could not hold the reins in your hands."

"I don't need to hold the reins, Father. If Mother will harness the horse to the cart and put me in the horse's ear, I'll simply tell the horse which way to go."

"Do you think it will work, Tom? Very well, we'll try!"

So late that afternoon, Tom's mother hitched the horse to the cart and put Tom Thumb in the horse's ear.

Tom waved goodbye. Then he shouted, "Gee up! Gee up!" and the horse started down the road, quite as if someone were sitting on the driver's seat, tugging at the reins and telling him which way to go.

As the horse was turning a corner going into the woods and Tom was shouting, "Gee up! Gee up!" two strangers passed by.

The first stranger said, "This is very odd. I see the horse, I hear the driver. But alas! I cannot see him!"

"This is very odd, indeed!" said the second stranger. "Let's follow that horse and cart and see to whom they belong."

The two strangers followed along until the horse reached the spot where the woodcutter worked.

Tom Thumb called out, "Whoa! Here I am, Father, with the horse and cart, just as I said. Come take me from the horse's ear."

The woodcutter lifted the little boy from the horse's ear and held him in the palm of his hand.

The two strangers were surprised to see Tom Thumb. They had never seen a child so small.

The first stranger said, "Let's buy that little boy and show him on the street corners in town. We'll make a fortune."

The second stranger said, "Didn't you hear? He's the woodcutter's son. The woodcutter will not sell his own son."

"Then let's take him," said the first stranger.
"There are two of us, but only one of them."

So the first stranger approached the woodcutter
and said, "Sell us that little boy, woodcutter. We'll
see that no harm comes to him."

"Oh no, no!" said the woodcutter. "I wouldn't
sell my own son."

But Tom Thumb had overheard the evil men
talking and quickly climbed up to his father's

shoulder and whispered in his ear, "You might as well take their gold, Father, because they plan to carry me off, anyway. But don't worry! I'll be home soon, very soon!"

And so it was that Tom Thumb was sold for a double handful of gold, and the tiny boy was carried away by the two strangers. He sat on the brim of the taller man's hat and watched the countryside as the strangers walked along the road.

At eventide, the two men were tired from having
walked so long and so far, and they sat down at
the crossroads to rest. Tom Thumb was tired, too,
from having sat so long, and he begged to be put
down upon the road to stretch his legs.

This was when the two strangers made their mistake! For when Tom Thumb was put down upon
the road, he darted off into a cornfield where he
found a mousehole just his size. And he slipped
down into it.

Just before he disappeared from sight, he called

out, "Goodbye, you evil men! Your gold has fallen into a mousehole! You'll never find me!"

The two men were angry. They ran up and down the rows of corn, punching sticks into every mousehole, but alas! they could not find Tom Thumb.

At last it became dark and the two men had to hurry on their way, because they knew their wives were waiting supper on them.

When Tom Thumb was certain that the two strangers had left, he crawled out of the mousehole. He didn't want to chance meeting a big ferocious animal, like a mouse, in its hole after dark. So he walked along a row of corn until he found a snail shell just his size. He curled up in it and fell asleep.

But no sooner was Tom Thumb asleep, than he was awakened by two robbers talking.

The first robber said, "Let's go to the rich man's house and steal his gold and silver."

The second robber said, "How can we get into his house? There are heavy iron bars at the window."

Tom Thumb called out, "I can help you!"

"Who said that?" asked the first robber.

"I did," said Tom Thumb. "I am right at the toe of your boot. Don't move your foot, you might step on me. Just follow the sound of my voice and you'll find me."

The first robber grabbed Tom Thumb and held him tight in his fist. "You little imp! How can you help us?"

"Oh, I can help you," said Tom. "You want someone to walk through the iron bars of the rich man's house and hand out his gold and silver? I am the very person who can do that."

The robber smiled. "Young man, you have quite a wit about you. We can use you!"

The robbers sneaked to the rich man's house and put Tom Thumb on the window sill. He was so small that he simply walked between the iron bars and made his way into the house.

As soon as he was out of reach of the robber's long arms, he called out loudly,

"WHAT DO YOU WANT FIRST,
THE GOLD OR THE SILVER?"

"Shhhhhh!" whispered the robbers. "Do you want to awaken everyone in the house, you little fool?"

"WHAT DO YOU WANT FIRST,
THE GOLD OR THE SILVER?"

The housemaid awakened. She lit a candle and came down the stairs, looking fearfully about. "What's going on down here?" she asked.

On hearing someone coming, the robbers turned and fled into the forest. They were never heard from again.

The housemaid looked all about, behind the doors and under the chairs, but she found no one. Tom Thumb was hidden behind an envelope on the rich man's desk.

Convinced at last that she had only been dreaming, the housemaid blew out her candle and went back to bed.

Tom Thumb waited until the house was quiet. Then he slipped down from the desk and out through the window. He made his way to the barn, where he found a nice warm spot in the hay and fell asleep.

When it was morning, a milkmaid came to the barn to feed and milk the cow. The first bundle of hay that she tossed into the cow's manger was the bundle in which Tom Thumb was sleeping.

When Tom awakened, he found himself in a cow's mouth, about to be chomped by the teeth!

He tried to escape but the cow's tongue pulled him back, and Tom Thumb found himself on a long slide, slipping down into the cow's stomach. When he reached the bottom, he looked around and said, "My, it's dark down here. When they made this place, they forgot to put in a window."

In the meantime, the cow was eating hay, and

the hay was coming down the slide into the stomach. It was too crowded for poor Tom. He called out, "No more hay, please! There's enough down here!"

Now, the milkmaid was seated on her milking stool, milking the cow. When she heard the cow speaking, she became so excited that she fell off her stool and spilled the bucket of milk.

The milkmaid ran to the house crying, "Master! Master, come quickly! The cow's gone crazy! The cow is talking!

"Not the cow, but you have lost your sense," said the rich man. However, he followed the milkmaid to the barn to see what was happening. As they came through the door, the cow was still saying, "No more hay, please! There's enough down here!"

The rich man now thought the cow was possessed by evil spirits, and he ordered the cow killed. The cow was slaughtered and her stomach was thrown out on a dunghill.

Tom was just freeing himself from the stomach, when out of the woods there came a great, gray, hungry wolf. With one gulp, he swallowed Tom Thumb!

Poor Tom! He was becoming discouraged. Troubles seemed to follow him wherever he went!

"Oh, Mr. Wolf!" he called out, "are you hungry?"

"Yes," said the wolf. "Wolves and boys are always hungry!"

"Then I can tell you where you can find some tasty food," said Tom. "Just follow the path through the woods to the woodcutter's cottage. Crawl through the drainpipe into the storeroom, and there you'll find ham and cheese and pickled eggs and smearcase and spiced beets and boiled pigs' feet. All of the good food that you could possibly want!"

The wolf didn't wait to be told twice where to find a meal, for his hunger was great. He ran down the path through the woods with his tail flying behind him and Tom Thumb riding in his stomach.

When the wolf came to the woodcutter's cottage, he did just as Tom had told him. He crawled through the drainpipe to the storeroom where he found all of the good food that Tom had described. The wolf ate and ate and ate . . . and ate . . . and . . . ate. At last he had his fill.

He turned back to the drainpipe to escape, but alas! he had grown so fat that he could not get out. This was exactly what Tom Thumb had counted on!

Tom called out, "Father! Father! Come save me! I'm home! I'm home! I'm home!"

Now Tom's voice didn't sound as loud as you might think, because, remember, Tom was inside of that wolf. His voice sounded more like this:

"Father! Father! Come save me! I'm home! I'm home! I'm home!"

Fortunately, Tom's father was a light sleeper. He heard Tom calling and he jumped out of bed. His wife was right behind him. They ran to the store-room and opened the door.

When they saw the wolf, the woodcutter grabbed an axe and his wife grabbed a butcher knife. Then they took after the wolf.

"Oh Father! Please be careful with that axe! I'm inside of this thing!"

Tom's father was careful, indeed. With one well-placed blow of the axe, he killed the wolf and Tom was rescued.

The woodcutter held Tom in the palm of his hand, and said, "Welcome home, Tom! Welcome home, son!"

Tom's mother was so happy that she began to cry. "Tom, Tom," she cried, "where have you been?"

"Mother, I've been in a mousehole, I've been in a snail's shell, I've been in a cow's stomach, and I've been inside of a wolf. But from now on I'm going to be happy just to stay home and sleep."

And that is exactly what Tom Thumb did. He curled up in his mother's thimble and he slept all of that morning and half of that afternoon — which is a long time for any boy to sleep.

Cows

Half the time they munched the grass,
  and all the time they lay
Down in the water-meadows,
  the lazy month of May,
    A-chewing,
    A-mooing,
To pass the hours away.

      "Nice weather," said the brown cow.
        "Ah," said the white.
      "Grass is very tasty."
        "Grass is all right."

Half the time they munched the grass,
  and all the time they lay
Down in the water-meadows,
  the lazy month of May,
    A-chewing,
    A-mooing,
To pass the hours away.

"Rain coming," said the brown cow.

"Ah," said the white.

"Flies is very tiresome."

"Flies bite."

Half the time they munched the grass,
and all the time they lay
Down in the water-meadows,
the lazy month of May,
A-chewing,
A-mooing,
To pass the hours away.

"Time to go," said the brown cow.

"Ah," said the white.

"Nice chat," "Very pleasant."

"Night." "Night."

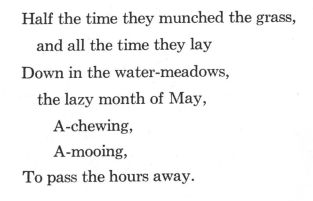

Half the time they munched the grass,
and all the time they lay
Down in the water-meadows,
the lazy month of May,
A-chewing,
A-mooing,
To pass the hours away.

by James Reeves,
picture by Mamoru Funai

Here's a Picture for Storytelling

by Kiyoaki Komoda

The Big Cheese

by Miriam Schlein,
pictures by Joseph Low

Once there was a farmer who made a big cheese.
It was yellow, and mellow, and round.
It was a most beautiful cheese.

"Without a doubt," said the farmer,
"this is the best cheese
that has ever been made in all the land."

"I think you are right," said his wife, taking a sniff.
"Take it to the market. It will fetch a good price."

"No," said the farmer.
"The best cheese in all the land—who should eat it?
Not just anybody! No," he said proudly.
"I am going to present this cheese to the king."

"The king!" said his wife. "To the king?"

"Of course," said the farmer.
"And even the king, when he has tasted,
will agree that this is the finest cheese
he has ever had in his life!"

He placed the big cheese carefully in a wheelbarrow.
His wife draped it over with a snowy white linen napkin.
And the farmer went down the road,
pushing the cheese before him.

He did not go too far, when he met a goatherd, herding along a flock of goats.

"What are you pushing along in that barrow, my friend?" called out the goatherd.

"A cheese," replied the farmer, setting down the wheelbarrow gently. "I am on my way to present it to the king, for it is the finest cheese that has ever been made in the land."

"Indeed?" said the goatherd. And is it made of goats' milk?"

"No," said the farmer. "Cows' milk."

"Then how," replied the goatherd, "can it be the best cheese ever made? The finest and richest and best cheeses are always made from goats' milk."

"How?" said the farmer indignantly. "This is how!" He flung the napkin off. And there sat the cheese— that beautiful, yellow, mellow cheese.

"It does look fine," agreed the goatherd. "But have you tasted it?"

"Of course not," said the farmer. "You can see it is still whole."

"Then how do you *know* it is the finest cheese ever made?

We must taste it, here and now,"
said the goatherd, pulling out a knife.

"Stop!" cried the farmer.
"How can I present the king with a cheese
that has a piece cut out of it?"

"But how can you
present the king with a cheese
you do not know tastes the best?"

"You are right," said the farmer. "Cut."

The goatherd cut out a large triangular slab.
This he cut in two,
half for the farmer, half for himself.

They each took a small taste.

"Indeed," sighed the goatherd.
"It is a fine-tasting cheese."

They sat in the shade, under a tree, nibbling cheese.
The goats nibbled the grass in a circle, all around them.

When they were finished, the farmer sprang up.
"I must be on my way," he said.

"I, too," said the goatherd. "Go well, my friend.
I must admit you have made the finest cheese
a man could make,
out of goats' milk, or cows' milk."

The farmer beamed.
He threw the napkin over the cheese and went on his way.
He followed the road over hill and dale.
As night began to fall, he came to an inn.

"I will stop here," he thought.
"I will have a bite to eat and get a good night's rest,
and early in the morning, I shall be on my way."

He pushed open the door,
which entered into a cheerful room,
all set with tables and cloths.
To one side, a big fire crackled in the fireplace.
Before the fire sat a fat, rather jolly-looking man.

"Come in," cried the fat man.
"The innkeeper is in the kitchen, fixing my meal.
But come warm yourself by the fire, my friend.
I am a traveler like yourself."

The farmer parked the barrow with the cheese
carefully away from the heat of the fire.

"And what have you there,
that you treat with such care?"
asked the man, curiously.

"I treat it with care indeed," replied the farmer.
"For this is a cheese, which I am taking to the king."

"To the king?" said the traveler.
"But the king has the most skilled cheese-makers
right at the palace!"

"But my cheese is the best
that has ever been made in the land," said the farmer.

"The best?" repeated the traveler. "How do you know?"

"I know," said the farmer, proudly.
"Besides, the goatherd agreed with me."

"The goatherd!" said the traveler.
"The goatherd may know about goats—
but what does he know of the king's taste for cheese?

"I tell you what," he went on. "Sit down. Relax.
Do me the honor of dining with me.
After we have wined and dined,
and our stomachs are contented,
then *we*," he said, pointing to himself,
"then *we* will taste your cheese.
For it does not do to taste cheese when one is very hungry.
For then almost anything will taste delicious.
No, the time to taste cheese for delicacy of flavor
is when the stomach is already contented.
That is the way to taste cheese.
Ask me, my friend. I know!"

"But I want to present my cheese to the king!"
cried the farmer.

"Of course," said the traveler. "Don't fear.
We will just take a teeny taste. It won't even be missed.
Come now," he beckoned. "Here is the dinner.
Sit down with me, and enjoy it."

The farmer sighed, and sat down.

Presently the innkeeper came
and set before them all sorts of steaming hot dishes.
One was a platter of roast duck,
all crispy and brown on the outside.
There was stuffing, and brown gravy with mushrooms.
There were buttery beans and carrots,
and a tray of fresh baked bread.
And to drink, there was a pitcher
of foamy homemade root beer.

"Ah," sighed the farmer, when they were finished.
"That was a meal to remember."

"And now," said the jolly traveler
sitting up in his chair, so that his big round body
seemed to fill every inch of it.
"Now we come to the treat of the meal.
Now we taste the cheese."

"The cheese," said the farmer.
"Are you sure you want to taste it now?
Aren't you a bit full?"

"Of course I'm full, of course," cried the jolly traveler.
"But if your cheese is as truly delicious as you say—
we will enjoy it even if we are full as full as full.
Bring it on!"
He whisked the napkin off the cheese.
"It *looks* good," he said.
Then he cut the cheese and took a small wedge.

He bit into the soft center,
and crushed the cheese on his tongue,
and swallowed.

"But the taste," he cried, striking the table.
"The taste is magnificent!
I have never tasted as good a cheese—
not even one made by myself!"

He wiped his hands of the crumbs.

"I must take another small piece."

"Mmmm," said the fat traveler,
with his mouth full.
"Mmmm. My friend," he said. "You are right.
This is a cheese fit for the king.
I'll take just one more taste.

"This is the last," promised the jolly traveler,
carving a large slice. "But here," he said.
"Don't you want a piece for yourself?
You haven't had any at all!"

"Oh, I'm too full," said the farmer unhappily,
as he watched his big cheese get smaller and smaller.

"There," said the fat traveling man, wiping his lips.
"Take it away."

The farmer leaped up, threw the napkin over the cheese,
and trundled it away. Then he said goodnight
and went up to his room to sleep.

In the morning early, the farmer awoke
and had a hearty breakfast.

Then he took his wheelbarrow, with the cheese,
and trundled it down the road.

It was a lovely day, sunny and bright.

The road led straight along.

The farmer walked briskly,
past field upon field of tall golden corn,
with tassels bending in the breeze.

And soon, in the distance,
he saw tall spires,
reaching into the sky.
"The king's palace,"
he said.

"I am there at last."

189

He straightened his shirt, pulled up his socks,
and presented himself at the palace gate.

"Who are you, and what do you carry?"
asked the guard at the gate.

"I am a farmer," said the farmer.
"And this is a cheese I have made for the king."

"That door," said the guard.
He pointed across the courtyard,
to where three young fellows were stringing beans,
and a woman was beating a batter.

"There is the royal kitchen."

"But this cheese is to be presented to the king himself!"
said the farmer, determinedly.

"Then that other door," said the guard.
He pointed to a high, arched doorway.

The farmer trundled across the courtyard
and through the high arched door.
He found himself alone in a large hall.

But from behind a closed doorway

at the other end of the hall, he heard a hum of voices.

Presently the door opened and a man came out.

He was dressed in elegant ribbons and silk,

with a plumed hat on his head.

When he saw the farmer and his barrow,

he said, surprised, "Eh, what is that?"

"A big cheese," said the farmer.

"I wish to present it to the king."

"A cheese, you say?" said the man with interest.

"Ah, a bit of cheese would taste good."

"Besides," he added, "I am the king's taster.

Whatever the king eats, I must taste first.

To make sure it is all right, you understand.

I had best do it now."

He bent down and with his silver penknife

cut off a wedge of the cheese.

"Indeed," he said, with his mouth full.

"It is a fine cheese."

"Now, may I present it to the king?" asked the farmer.

The taster's mouth was too full to answer.

Just then, the door opened again

and another man came out.

He was even more elegantly dressed than the first,

in varying shades of deep maroon,

with tassels and braids of gold.

"What are you doing?" he asked in amazement,
seeing the farmer with the barrow,
and the first man with his silver penknife in hand.

"Cheese," the first man managed to say. "Very good."

"Ah," said the second man,
unclasping a little gold penknife, and making a cut.

Another, then another of the king's men came out.
Soon there were seven, all standing about,
with their delicate little knives in hand,
all munching on the cheese.

Presently still another man came out
from the room at the end of the hall,
closing the door behind him.

He was of medium height, the same as the farmer.
He had a ruddy face, as if he spent
much of his time out of doors.

And he was not dressed as splendidly
as the other men of the court.
but the other men stepped back
when he approached. "What is this?" he said.

"A cheese, sir," said the farmer, stepping forward.
"The best that has ever been made in all the land.
And who should eat the best cheese?
Not just anybody. No.
It is a cheese fit for a king.
And that is why I am here.
I have come to present it to the king!"

"Indeed?" said the ruddy-faced man, lifting the napkin.
The farmer stared. For what was left of his big cheese?
Not a half. Not even a quarter.
Just a small piece stood there, amidst the crumbles.

The ruddy-faced man bent down,
and reached for the last piece.

"Stop!" cried the farmer.
His voice rang out in the large hall.
"Stop, stop, STOP!"

The others looked up in amazement.

"Excuse me," said the farmer, sadly.
"But I meant this cheese for the king.
And you are taking the very last piece.
Well, take it," he said, turning sadly.

"It doesn't matter now.

I traveled all this way,

but I can't present the king with just a scrap.

Go on," he said. "Finish it."

"But I am the king," the ruddy-faced man said, softly.

"The king!" said the farmer. "A thousand pardons!"

He bent his head, and fell to one knee,

nearly tipping the barrow as he did so.

"Come," said the king. "Get up.

A thousand pardons? A thousand pardons for what?

For your loyalty to the king?

For wishing to present to him the finest cheese

you have ever made in your life?

"Come now," he said.

"There is nothing to pardon. Get up."

The farmer got up, all red in the face.

"May I have this last piece of cheese now?"
asked the king with a smile.

"I do love cheese, you know."

"Of course," the farmer nodded.

The king ate the piece of cheese.

"It is the finest cheese I have ever tasted
in all my life!" he said.

"And I thank you."

The farmer beamed. "But such a small piece was left,"
he said. "I am sorry."

"Look here," said the king.

"This is not the last cheese
you will ever make in your life, is it?"

"No." The farmer shook his head.

"Well then," said the king,
"when you make another cheese
which you feel you would like me to have,
just bring it around.

And do not let anyone taste it first," he added.

"I will trust your very own judgment."

To this the farmer agreed.

Then he trundled his empty wheelbarrow back home,
whistling all the way.

How glad he was to be home!
He told his wife his adventures.
Then he busied himself on his farm
with his chickens, and his soft brown cows,
and his asparagus and pumpkin garden.
And of course, he made cheeses.

They were fine cheeses, yellow
and mellow and round.
But somehow, none seemed yellow
and mellow enough so as to be fit for a king.

Many months passed. Almost a year.
Then one day, the farmer ran in, to his wife.

"I have made one!" he cried. "At last!"

"Fit for a king?" asked his wife.

"Fit for a king!"

With not another word,
they placed the big cheese on the wheelbarrow.
The farmer's wife covered it
with a gleaming white linen napkin.

And the farmer set off, down the road,
to the palace of the king.

Not the goatherd,
nor the jolly traveler,
nor the king's own men,
nor anyone else took a taste of *this* cheese.

This cheese the farmer presented to the king
round, and complete, and unbroken.

It was every bit as good as the first one.
It was a cheese fit for a king!

That is what the king said.
And he should know!

The Park

I'm glad that I
Live near a park

For in the winter
After dark

The park lights shine   As dandelions
As bright and still   On a hill.

by James S. Tippett, picture by Gilbert Riswold

Here's a Picture for Storytelling

by Symeon Shimin

When Christmas Comes

by Doris Whitman,
pictures by David K. Stone

For three days it snowed without stopping. The Mallorys couldn't remember when it had snowed so much. All the schools were closed. Snow plows had broken down because the snow was so heavy. It was a real snowstorm.

Sara and Tim Mallory talked excitedly as the flakes drifted down. But their brother Jake didn't seem to care. He didn't look up when Tim ran into his bedroom.

"Did you hear the news?" Tim asked, his brown eyes shining. "We're not going to buy a Christmas tree this year. We're going to cut our own! One of those," he said, pointing to the two spruce trees outside Jake's window. "How do you like that?"

Jake shrugged. "It's all right," he said.

"You can watch from the window," said Tim, trying to get his brother interested. "I'll yell 'Timmmberr,' so you'll know when it's coming down.

Jake said nothing, and went on reading.

Jake felt so left out of it all! He felt none of the excitement of their having their own tree. He couldn't help cut it, and he hated the idea of sitting at the window watching the others have the fun. He decided he wouldn't watch them cut it down, and he wouldn't help decorate it either. He didn't want to have anything to do with their Christmas tree!

Jake had been very ill when he was six years old. Now he was ten. He still wore braces on his legs and he had to sit in a wheel chair. He would never be able to run and play as other children did, but the doctors had said he might walk again if he really tried. At first Jake seemed to accept this and learned to take a few steps on his own. But as Sara and Tim got older and Jake heard them tell of all the adventures they had, he began to lose interest in walking. He seemed to feel that if he couldn't do all the things the others did, there was no point in walking at all.

Mr. Mallory, Tim, and Sara went out to cut the tree on Sunday. Wrapped in scarves and mufflers, carrying peanut butter sandwiches to fortify themselves, they tramped out into the snow.

With much laughing and pulling and pushing
they brought it at last, full of snow, onto the porch.
"Now you can start on the decorations," said Mr.
Mallory. "Tomorrow we'll bring the tree inside."

Later
that afternoon,
Sara took
colored paper
and scissors in to Jake.
"No thanks," said Jake,
as she entered the room.
"I don't want to make
decorations this year."

"Why not?" asked Sara, disappointed. "You always make such good ones."

But Jake just shook his head and turned away.
Sara was about to go out, when suddenly
Jake said, "Look!"

He was pointing to the one spruce tree still standing outside his window. "Chickadees!"

Sara ran over to see. The tree was full of little birds. They were hopping in and out of the branches, chirping away, as merry as could be.

"They look so happy," said Jake. "Look how they're jumping around!"

"Those two are fighting over something," said Sara. "Look, Jake! It's Tim's peanut butter sandwich! He must have dropped it when we were cutting down the tree."

They spent the rest of the afternoon watching the little birds. They stood at the window until it was too dark to see any more.

The next morning the snow had stopped, and everything was lovely. The sky was clear and blue, and everything else was white. In some places only the very tops of the bushes could be seen. The sunlight glistened on the icicles. It was a wonderful sea of sparkling snow outside.

After breakfast Sara ran to the window to see if the chickadees were playing in the spruce tree. But the tree was empty, and there, lying in the snow, were four little birds.

Sara ran as fast as she could to Jake's room, holding back her tears. "Jake! Jake! Four of those little chickadees are dead! Someone killed them!"

Jake quickly wheeled his chair to the window and looked out at the four dark spots on the snow.

His face turned pale. "No one killed them," he said quietly. "They were hungry. That's why they died."

"But we saw them yesterday, eating Tim's sandwich," said Sara.

"That's just it," said Jake. "That's why there were so many of them yesterday. They all wanted some of the sandwich. But there wasn't enough to go around."

Sara burst into tears. "Oh, Jake," she said. "I thought those little birds were happy, and all that time they were starving!"

"We should have put some crumbs out for them," Jake said, half to himself. Suddenly he swung his chair around to face Sara. "Don't just stand there crying!" he shouted. "Go and put some food out for them! We don't want any more dying around here!"

Sara rushed off to the kitchen, without another word. She pulled on her snow pants and jacket, and waded out into the snow.

As she came close to the spot where the little birds were lying, she thought she saw one of them move. She picked it up carefully and held it in her hands. She was sure she could feel it breathing. Scattering the breadcrumbs on top of the snow, she hurried back to Jake.

"This one's alive!" she said breathlessly, carefully handing the little bird to Jake. Jake held it in his hand and his eyes widened with excitement. The little heart was beating!

"Sara!" he said. "You're right! It *is* alive!" He put the bird inside his bathrobe, holding it against his

chest. "We've got to warm it, and we've got to get some food into it, too."

"I'll get some breadcrumbs," said Sara.

"No, wait a minute!" said Jake. "It won't eat breadcrumbs now. Here, I'll try this." He took some hot cereal from his untouched breakfast tray and forced the food into the bird's mouth.

Its little head flopped to one side, and the hot cereal slid down its throat. Jake fed the bird four or

five times. Sara stood watching, almost afraid to
breathe.

Jake could feel his own heart beating as he put
the bird back inside his bathrobe. "Please don't let
it die," he wished silently.

"Sara, see if you can find a small box," he said
aloud. "And get some seeds and water."

"Do you think it will live?" asked Sara in a
whisper.

"I think so," said Jake. "But I need something to put it in. Hurry!"

In a very short time Sara was back, and she was carrying a shoe box with cotton, a handful of sunflower seeds, and a small cup of water in the bottom. Jake gently placed the chickadee on the soft cotton and Sara put the box on the radiator. They leaned over the box, watching the little bird closely. After a few moments it began to move.

"Jake! Did you see?" whispered Sara excitedly. "It moved."

"I know," said Jake, his eyes shining. "It's going to get well."

After lunch, Tim came to join the watch over the little bird. "Jake really saved it," Sara said proudly. "He knew just what to feed it, and what to do with it."

"But what about the other birds?" asked Tim. "We'd better feed them too, or more will die. We can put the food in the tree. That way they'll be able to get at it."

"Oh, let's do that," said Sara, clapping her hands. "We can tie the food onto the branches."

So they all helped to string apples and oranges and popcorn balls, and Tim and Sara went back and forth, carrying things outside to put in the tree. At the end of an hour the tree was laden, and the young Mallorys could be sure that no more birds would die in their yard. There were cups of birdseed, lumps of suet, peanut butter in tin-foil cups, and mush. There were pumpkin seeds and sunflower seeds, raisins and peanuts, popcorn balls, apples and oranges strung from the branches.

"Look, Tim!" cried Sara, as they finished. "It's a Christmas tree for the birds!"

Jake was laughing as they walked into his room. "Take a look at those silly birds," he said. "They're as good as a circus."

Sara and Tim ran over to his window to look. The tree was a-flutter with birds. Chickadees and blue jays were flying in and out of the branches, chattering and scolding at each other.

"What's the matter with them?" asked Tim.

"The blue jays want all the food for themselves," said Jake. "They're chasing the chickadees away."

"Why don't they all eat together?" asked Sara.

"The sassy things! Go away! Shoo!" shouted Sara to the blue jays.

"They're hungry, too," said Jake. "Do you want them to die like the others? Our little birds will come back after awhile. Just watch, you'll see!"

A squeak from the box on the radiator made them all turn around. They were just in time to see the little chickadee hop to the corner of the box and take a peck at the birdseed.

"He's getting better, all right," said Tim. "He's going to fly out of here soon. We'd better get a cage, if we want to keep him."

"No, you can't do that!" said Jake angrily. "This is a wild bird! He's used to being free, and he'd die if you put him in a cage."

"Gee, Jake," said Sara, "You really know a *lot* about birds."

Dinner was very gay that night. Everyone was happy because Jake had come to the table. For months he'd been having his meals in his room, all alone. He had felt that he couldn't share in the fun and laughter of the others. But today things were different. Jake had things to tell, too. He was full of excitement from the day's adventures. So they all

laughed together at dinner again, and Jake talked as much as anyone.

When the meal was over, Mrs. Mallory said, "Now that the birds have their Christmas tree, I think it's time for us to begin on ours. Are you coming to help, Jake?"

"Sure thing!" said Jake.

So it seemed that the holiday season, which had started out so badly, was full of hope after all.

The next afternoon, Sara and her mother were
frosting cookies in the kitchen, and Tim was putting the wreath up on the door. Suddenly there was
a great shout, "Tim! Sara! Somebody come here
quickly!"

It was Jake. They all dropped everything and
ran to his room.

"There's a hawk after some of the birds!" he cried, when they came to the door. "He'll eat the little ones if he catches them. Please, chase him away!"

But no one moved. They all stood in the doorway, staring at Jake. He was *standing* at the window!"

"Please, hurry!" cried Jake. "They don't even see him yet."

"I'll get him, Jake," said Tim, starting forward. "I'll get the broom."

They all watched from the window as Tim dashed out into the snow. He shouted and shook the broom at the hawk. After a few minutes it flapped its wings lazily and flew off.

When the hawk was gone and Tim was back inside Mother said, "Jake, do you know that you are standing up? You've been standing—alone—all this time!"

"I . . . I didn't even know it!" said Jake, staring at them. "I'm standing . . . and I didn't even know. It must have happened when I saw the hawk."

And then they were all laughing and talking at once. But Jake didn't say another word. He just stood very still and thought, "I'm going to do this every day, and then, when Christmas comes . . ."

And Christmas was coming quickly now. There were secrets and whisperings throughout the house, and every now and then you could hear the crinkly sounds of wrapping paper. Every day more presents appeared under the tree. It was hard not to take a peek, or feel the packages just a little.

The last few days before Christmas, Jake's door was closed most of the time. The others might have thought it strange, but they were so busy they hardly noticed. And it was just as well, because behind his closed door, Jake was busy, too.

At last, it was here! It was Christmas morning.

"Merry Christmas!" cried Mrs. Mallory, as she went in to Jake's room to help him to his chair. "Merry..." and she stopped short, for there was Jake, sitting in his chair.

"Jake!" cried Mrs. Mallory, in amazement. "How did you get there?"

"Merry Christmas, Mom," said Jake, smiling. And then, before Mrs. Mallory could say another word, Jake lifted himself from the chair, and slowly took three steps toward her. "Mom," he said, "if you'll help me, I'm going to walk to the Christmas tree."

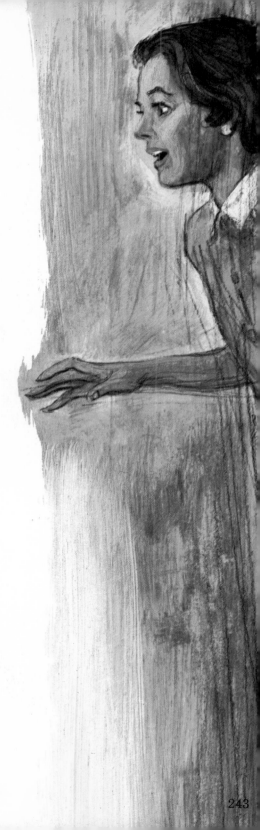

You should have seen the faces of the other Mallorys when Jake walked slowly into the living room, leaning on Mrs. Mallory's arm.

"Jake!" cried Mr. Mallory, rushing towards him.

"You're walking!" shouted Tim.

"Oh, Jake," said Sara, throwing her arms around him, and laughing and crying at once. "You can walk again! How did it ever happen?"

Jake hugged her happily. "Well, almost anything . . .

. . . can happen   when Christmas comes!"

Stopping by Woods
on a Snowy Evening

by Robert Frost,
picture by Ed Young

Whose woods these are I think I know.
His house is in the village though;
He will not see me stopping here
To watch his woods fill up with snow.

My little horse must think it queer
To stop without a farmhouse near
Between the woods and frozen lake
The darkest evening of the year.

He gives his harness bells a shake
To ask if there is some mistake.
The only other sounds' the sweep
Of easy wind and downy flake.

The woods are lovely, dark, and deep.
But I have promises to keep,
And miles to go before I sleep,
And miles to go before I sleep.

Here's a Picture for Storytelling or Writing a Poem

by Thomas M. O'Brien

12 Rules of the Road

by the Bicycle Institute of America,
pictures by Herbert McClure

Here are twelve rules of the road that have been approved by the Bicycle Institute of America. If you are a bicycle rider, you will want to know and do something about these rules.

1. Make sure brakes are functioning smoothly. Keep your bike in perfect operating condition.

2. Keep to the right and ride in a straight line. Always ride in single file.

3. Always use proper hand signals when turning or stopping.

4. Have a working signal device, such as a horn or bell.

5. Slow down and look to the right and left at all intersections.

6. Look out for parked cars or cars pulling into traffic. Watch for doors opening on parked cars.

7. Obey all traffic regulations, signs, and lights.

8. Don't weave in and out of traffic or swerve from side to side.

9. Give pedestrians the right of way. Avoid riding on the sidewalk.

10. Do not carry passengers or objects which interfere with your vision or control.

11. Never hitch a ride on other vehicles. Never do stunts, or race in traffic.

12. Have a white light on the front of the bike and a red light or reflector on the back, and always wear light-colored clothing at night.

The Well-Equipped Bicycle

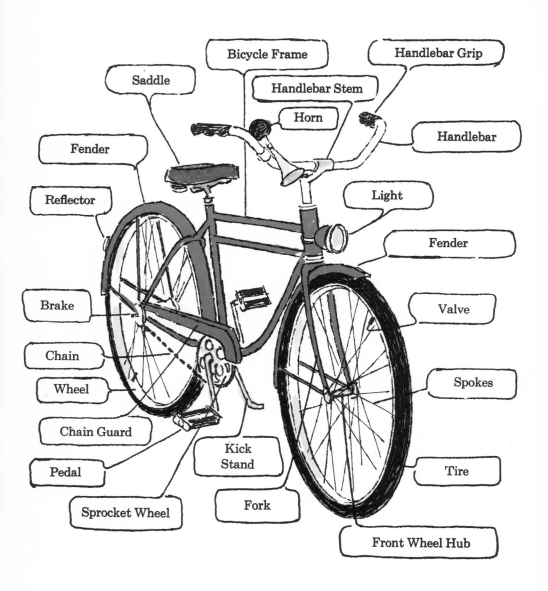

Bicycle Frame

Handlebar Grip

Saddle

Handlebar Stem

Horn

Handlebar

Fender

Light

Reflector

Fender

Brake

Valve

Chain

Wheel

Spokes

Chain Guard

Kick Stand

Pedal

Tire

Sprocket Wheel

Fork

Front Wheel Hub

Never Carry Great Big Things

Jill Grossman

Lawrence Grossman

Not too fast

Nev - er car - ry great big things when you're on your bike. Great big things are hard to car - ry, That means big things like: peo - ple, pack- a - ges, pen - guins, po -lar bears, pump - kins, pan-das and such! You won't be ab -le to see a thing, and they weigh much too much!

Poor Old Lady

1: Poor old lady, she swallowed a fly,
   I don't know why she swallowed a fly.
2: Poor old lady, I think she'll die.

3: Poor old lady, she swallowed a spider.
   It squirmed and wriggled and turned inside her.
1: She swallowed the spider to catch the fly.
   I don't know why she swallowed a fly.
2: Poor old lady, I think she'll die.

4: Poor old lady, she swallowed a bird.
   How absurd! She swallowed a bird.
3: She swallowed the bird to catch the spider,
2: She swallowed the spider to catch the fly,
   I don't know why she swallowed a fly.
1: Poor old lady, I think she'll die.

5: Poor old lady, she swallowed a cat.
   Think of that! She swallowed a cat.
4: She swallowed the cat to catch the bird.
3: She swallowed the bird to catch the spider,
1: She swallowed the spider to catch the fly,
   I don't know why she swallowed a fly.
2: Poor old lady, I think she'll die.

The numbers are for reading the poem aloud in parts.
Each number tells you when a new person reads.

254

6: Poor old lady,

      she swallowed a dog.

She went the whole hog

     when she swallowed the dog.

5: She swallowed the dog to catch the cat,

4: She swallowed the cat to catch the bird,

3: She swallowed the bird to catch the spider,

1: She swallowed the spider to catch the fly.

I don't know why she swallowed a fly.

2: Poor old lady, I think she'll die.

7: Poor old lady,

    . she swallowed a cow.

I don't know how

    she swallowed the cow.

6: She swallowed the cow to catch the dog,

5: She swallowed the dog to catch the cat,

4: She swallowed the cat to catch the bird,

3: She swallowed the bird to catch the spider,

1: She swallowed the spider to catch the fly,

I don't know why she swallowed a fly.

2: Poor old lady, I think she'll die.

8: Poor old lady,

    she swallowed a horse.

All: She died, of course.

author unknown,
pictures by Robert Jon Antler

A Fox Story

by Allan Sollers,
pictures by William Reusswig

This is a true story. It began one noontime when
I was a boy in a country school in Calvert County,
Maryland. The day was sunny and cool, just right
for a ball game or a chase through the woods.

We rushed noisily out of the school door when
Miss Elaine dismissed us—the big boys first, followed
by the girls and smaller children. There were sixteen
of us in school, ranging from first to eighth graders.

Suddenly, Charles stopped and held up his
hands for silence. Because he was the strongest and
smartest boy in school, the rest of us immediately
obeyed. He said nothing, but his expression told us
to be patient.

He cocked his head to one side, listening. Then
he asked, "Do you hear that? Them's hounds!"

There was no mistaking the sound of hounds on the trail of a fox. Each of us had heard this familiar sound most of our lives, because fox hunting was a favorite sport in Calvert County.

"I'll bet they're coming this way," Charles said breathlessly.

"The last time they chased that fox, he crossed through the cornfield and ran right down to Rawlings Cove," I said. Capt'n Jim, who never missed a hunt if he could help it, had told me about the last one when the fox had outsmarted the hounds along the north shore of the cove.

"Let's go!" Henry shouted. "Maybe the fox is headed for the cove again!"

"It sounds like it!" exclaimed Charles.

Charles took off across the schoolyard with Henry close behind him. The rest of us upper-grade boys followed, each carrying his lunch sack.

"What about us?" the girls shouted.

"We'll tell you all about it when we get back!" Charles answered.

It was an unwritten law that the girls and the smaller boys never followed us when we took to the woods during the noon hour. This was one of the privileges that we older boys enjoyed, the right to have some time to ourselves.

Charles and Henry led the way through the woods to the fence that bordered the lower end of the cornfield. When we arrived at the fence, the pack of hounds was much closer.

"The fox is coming this way for sure," Tom whispered.

"If Capt'n Jim finds us here, he'll skin us alive," I said. "He has no use for kids on a fox hunt."

Charles had the same idea. We were uninvited guests, and this was no time to meet the hunters face to face. He turned quickly to climb a huge pine tree that grew near the fence. The rest of us followed up the stair-step limbs and climbed quickly to the tree-top. There we settled down in our majestic grand-stand to wait for whatever might happen.

We opened our sacks to eat our lunches, but we were careful not to make any noise. The hounds were still some distance away, although we could tell that the fox was leading them to Rawlings Cove.

Then, heavenly days! A full-grown red fox trotted out of the bushes just to the left of us and stopped at the edge of the field, looking in the direction of the hounds. The fox was not more than fifty yards away. All of us saw him at the same moment.

Fortunately, the wind was in our favor. The fox obviously had not caught our scent. He stood calmly, unalarmed by the approach of the dogs.

His actions were puzzling. It looked as if he were waiting for the hounds instead of running from them. His unruffled coat and his brisk step showed no signs of weariness. I knew that we were seeing a fox use all of his cunning to avoid the dogs, but just what he was up to baffled me.

A moment later
we were even more confused.
A second fox appeared at the edge of the cornfield. This fox was much smaller than the first, and was apparently the vixen mate of the first fox. She was wet, muddy, and obviously weary. There was no doubt that this second fox was the one the hounds were trailing.

Coming along the edge of the cornfield, the vixen ran directly to her mate. She brushed against him, and then ran to a gap in the fence that surrounded the field. She leaped to the top rail of the log fence and, like a tightrope walker, moved quickly along until she vanished from sight.

In spite of the fact that the pack of dogs was coming quite close, the male fox showed no alarm. With calm deliberateness,
he flattened down on his stomach
and began crawling on the grass.

He continued moving in this fashion toward the fence where his mate had leaped from the ground to the top rail. After he had passed five or six feet beyond this point, he leaped to his feet and flashed away toward the cove.

All of us had heard that foxes would relieve each other when they were being chased by hounds. Here we had seen it happen! The male fox had come to the rescue of his mate and was deliberately leading the dogs in another direction! We were greatly impressed by the way in which the fox had made sure that the hounds would follow him instead of his tired mate.

Suddenly, the pack of hounds burst out of the woods with frenzied baying. They followed the scent of the fox along the edge of the cornfield and to the gap in the fence. In a few moments, they had passed beneath us and were off chasing the male fox to the cove. Not one of them caught the scent of the vixen that had escaped them by running along the top of the rail fence.

The hunters arrived quickly, following the dogs. They passed below us without knowing that we had viewed them from our treetop seats.

When we were certain that they were gone, we scrambled down the tree in wild amazement. We ran to the fence and viewed at close range the rails along which the vixen had traveled.

"Wasn't that something" Henry said in breathless admiration.

"Wait 'til the kids hear about this!" said Charles.

A clanging schoolbell summoned us back through the woods which stood between the cornfield and the schoolyard. The excitement with which we told the story of seeing the fox hunt caused everyone to gather around us. Miss Elaine encouraged us to tell in detail what we had seen. For more than a half hour we recounted each of the details. Then Miss Elaine reminded us that we should get on with our studies. It was hard to settle down to arithmetic with the memory of the foxes so fresh in our minds.

The next day after school, Charles signaled to us. We knew by his actions that a secret communication was to be delivered, so we followed him to the edge of the schoolyard.

"I heard the men talking down at the store last night," Charles began. "They are going fox hunting again on Saturday."

"Capt'n Jim said that the fox outsmarted him yesterday," I added. "He's bound to catch that fox if it's the last thing he ever does."

"The men plan to bring in another pack of hounds," Charles said.

"Well, what about it?" asked Henry. "Is there any chance that they'll take us along?"

"No, they'll never change their minds about us," Charles answered. "The best that we can hope for is another look at the fox like yesterday. Let's plan to meet down at the cove to see what the fox does when he gets there."

"I can't go on Saturday," I explained. "That's a work day. My mom has a lot of things laid out for me to do."

"Getting away on Saturday will be hard for all of us," Charles agreed. "But tell your mothers that I've invited you up to my house Saturday. Beg hard! We don't want to miss seeing the foxes again."

"Oh, we'll be there, all right," said Henry. "Saturday work or no, we'll be there."

"We'll all meet at my house and go to the south shore of Rawlings Cove," Charles added. "We can sit in them big trees down there and see what happens."

"Everybody better bring along something to eat," said Henry. "We won't be getting much lunch, more than likely."

When our plans to view the fox hunt on Saturday were complete, our group meeting broke up and we started home.

On Saturday, six of us who had gained our mothers' consent gathered at Charles's house at the appointed hour. We waited thirty minutes longer to make sure that no one would be left behind. Then we headed for the cove. Henry looked at his watch. It was almost eleven o'clock. Most of us knew the time anyway, by the empty feeling in our stomachs and by the position of the sun in the sky.

"We'll catch thunder if Capt'n Jim finds us spying on him," I said.

"He won't find us," Charles said. "We'll be careful."

"He'll blister us good if we interfere with the hunt, but it will be worth it to see the foxes again," Henry said with a nervous laugh.

We moved quietly to the cove and climbed up a big tree on the south side of the water. We agreed that no one would call out or say anything, no matter what happened. Each of us had brought a couple of apples which we slipped out of our pockets and began eating as silently as we could.

Our timing was excellent! Shortly after we were settled in the treetop, we heard the hounds trailing the fox. Their baying steadily became louder. Charles gave a signal for all of us to remain perfectly still, and pointed to the opposite side of the cove where the fox might first appear.

Our tension mounted as we watched intently for the first sign of the fox. The baying of the hounds indicated that he was coming closer all the time.

Suddenly, the fox broke from the bushes at a dead run! He crossed the clearing between the bushes and the shore in a flash.

When he reached the edge of the water, he made a tremendous leap into the creek! It looked to me as if the fox had jumped at least twenty feet! Charles said later that he was sure the leap had been longer than that.

In any event, when the fox hit the water, he began to swim up the cove and out from the shore. We thought he was swimming around a fallen, giant pine tree whose thick, downward limbs held the trunk a few feet above the water. The fox, however, had a different idea.

When he reached the outer end of the tree, he turned and swam in among its branches. He moved in close under the tree trunk, then disappeared from sight. Obviously, he had flattened himself against one of the big limbs, with only the tip of his nose above the water. In this position, he would be most difficult for the hounds to find.

Soon the hunters and the hounds arrived. There was a great commotion. The hounds broke into the clearing, and eagerly sniffed the scent of the fox up to the water's edge. Then they lost it. Both dogs and men moved up and down the shore, seeking the track or scent of the fox. But not a trace of their quarry did they find.

Then Capt'n Jim's most dependable hound, Old Belle, jumped upon the trunk of the fallen tree and began to follow it out from the shore.

"Oh, go back, old hound, go back!" was my silent prayer. I was sure that my companions felt the same as I did.

The hound was now halfway out to the end of the tree trunk! My blood pounded in my veins as I contemplated the fate of the fox. Was the fox holding his breath as I was? Could Old Belle see the fox submerged in the water? Could she possibly smell the fox's breath at that distance? Would the hound work her way out to the end of the tree trunk, or would the protruding limbs stop her?

As if in answer to our prayers, the hound stopped. She slowly turned around and started back toward the shore.

Momentarily, the fox seemed safe. Then a hunter asked, "Do you suppose the fox is out on that old tree?"

"No," replied Capt'n Jim. "That was my best hound. Old Belle would have spotted that fox if he was in the vicinity of that tree. I think that fox swam the creek. I'll take my hounds around the head of the cove and down the other shore. You fellows follow this shoreline down, and one of us should find the spot where the fox left the water to go back in the woods."

Once again I prayed, "Oh, Fox, don't move too soon!"

Capt'n Jim and his hounds were coming around the head of the cove. They were going to pass the tree in which we were hidden. We breathed deeply and prepared for the moment of the passing. Even if they found us now, I wouldn't care. The fox was safe. What would we say if they found us? My fears were unnecessary, for Capt'n Jim and his hounds passed below us without a moment's hesitation.

When each party had examined the shoreline without finding a trace of the fox, they made new plans.

"That scamp got away again," Capt'n Jim called to his friends. "I think he followed the swamp up toward Murray's farm. Take the road on your side and meet me at the schoolhouse."

Then they were gone. Minutes passed before the fox moved. Finally, we noticed a slight ripple in the water where the fox had hidden. He raised his head above the surface. He made no sound. When he was sure that he was safe, he swam back down the cove to the spot where he had entered the water. He crawled up on a flat rock that lay quite close to the shore, and shook the water from his fur. After looking cautiously about, he leaped from the rock to the grass and was gone.

Then Charles gave the signal to break silence. We all started chattering at once. We climbed down the tree, elated by the fox's cunning.

"That's the smartest fox I ever knew," said Henry.

"And we won't ever tell his secret," said Charles. "Let's all pledge that we won't tell his hiding place."

As far as I know, not one of us boys ever broke the pledge in the fox's lifetime.

Four Little Foxes

Speak gently, Spring, and make no sudden sound;
For in my windy valley, yesterday I found
New-born foxes squirming on the ground—
    Speak gently.

Walk softly, March, forbear the bitter blow;
Her feet within a trap, her blood upon the snow,
The four little foxes saw their mother go—
    Walk softly.

Go lightly, Spring, oh, give them no alarm;
When I covered them with boughs to shelter them
    from harm,
The thin blue foxes suckled at my arm—
    Go lightly.

Step softly, March, with your rampant hurricane;
Nuzzling one another, and whimpering with pain,
The new little foxes are shivering in the rain—
    Step softly.

by Lew Sarett